Robinson Crusoe

Retold by
Stewart Ross

Illustrated by
Vince Reid

ARCTURUS

For Max Macdonald, with love—SR.

For Patricia, my Mum—VR.

ARCTURUS

This edition published in 2018 by Arcturus Publishing Limited
26/27 Bickels Yard, 151–153 Bermondsey Street,
London SE1 3HA

Writer: Stewart Ross
Illustrator: Vince Reid
Designer: Jeni Child
Editor: Sebastian Rydberg
Art Director: Jessica Crass

ISBN: 978-1-78828-689-3
CH006283NT
Supplier 24, Date 0318, Print run 6733

Printed in Malaysia

Contents

CHAPTER 1

Leaving Home

My name is Robinson Crusoe, and this is the true story of my life and adventures. First, I'll explain my name. My mother's family name was "Robinson." My father came from Germany, and his family name was "Kreutznaer." To help his English friends, he changed it to "Crusoe."

I was born in York, England, in 1632, the youngest of three brothers. The eldest was killed in the wars, and my other brother just disappeared. We were clearly not a lucky family.

Because of this, my parents told me not to do anything

foolish. "Don't go on adventures," my father advised. "Stay in York, and get a good, sensible job as a lawyer."

But you know what young people are like, don't you? I did the opposite of what my parents told me.

In 1651, when I was just nineteen, I went to the port of Hull. There, I met a friend who was about to sail to London in his father's ship. "Come on, Robinson," he urged, "join me! It'll be really exciting!"

The temptation was too great to resist. Without even telling my parents what I was doing, I boarded ship on the first of September, and set sail for London.

My friend said the voyage would be exciting—and he was certainly right! No sooner had we left Hull than the wind began to blow hard, and the sea rose in waves as tall as the Yorkshire hills.

I was terrified. *This is a punishment from God for disobeying my parents*, I thought. I promised myself that, if I survived, I would go straight home and never venture to sea again.

How foolish I was! The wind died down, the sun came out, and I quickly forgot my promise. I had great fun laughing and singing with the sailors.

You can never, ever trust the sea. After a period of calm, the wind rose once more. This time it was much, much stronger. Our ship pitched and rolled in the storm, and started to leak.

I worked frantically at the pumps, trying to keep us from sinking.

We had almost given up hope when another vessel came in sight. Desperately, we waved for help. They launched a small boat, and we managed to scramble into it.

Safe on board the rescue ship, we watched in horror as the sea smashed our vessel to pieces, and it sank beneath the angry waves.

I was pretty shaken and scared when we finally made it to Yarmouth. Seeing me in this state, my friend's father came up and gave me a stern look.

"Young Master Robinson Crusoe," he said, "one thing is clear to me."

"Yes, sir," I answered, "and what is it?"

"You are not a seafaring man," he explained. "You should never go to sea again. If you do, I prophesy you will meet with nothing but disasters and disappointments."

In my heart of hearts, I knew he was right. The sensible thing would be to go home. But once more, I didn't do the sensible thing. Having a bit of money in my pocket, I decided to go to London.

To be honest, I was too ashamed to return to my parents. It would mean

admitting they'd been right.
I couldn't face that
and set out on
the high road.

Once I got
to the great city,
all thoughts of
going back to
York vanished from my mind. London
was a wonderful place, full of interest and
excitement, and I soon made new friends.
I also had a chance to make money.

One of my new London friends was an honest sea captain. He was an amiable man, and we got along really well.

One day, as we drank a beer together, he said, "I have a proposal, Robinson. Next week, I'm going trading in Africa. Fancy coming with me?"

I remembered my last voyage and hesitated.

"Come on," said the captain. "You can trade, too. You might even get rich!"

That settled it. With the forty pounds I had, I bought goods the captain told me would be popular in Africa. With everything safely on board, we set sail for Guinea. To my relief, though I was horribly seasick, we arrived without meeting a single storm.

In the markets of Guinea, I found I had

a knack for trading. The local people loved the things I brought. I swapped them for a pile of gold dust.

The return trip went well. As soon as we had tied up in the London docks, I hurried to a merchant with my gold. What was it worth? I asked eagerly.

The goldsmith weighed it and said it was worth three hundred pounds: I had turned forty pounds into three hundred in just a few months!

Shortly after our return to London, to my great sorrow, the captain died. However, I decided to continue trading. I gave two hundred pounds to the captain's widow and asked her to invest it for me. The other hundred pounds I took with me on another trip to Guinea.

This time, my luck ran out. Near the Canary Islands, we were chased by a large pirate ship. The enemy was faster than us, and we had to fight.

The battle was between our twelve cannon and the pirates' eighteen. At first, we held them off. But they came alongside with a crafty move, and sixty pirates swarmed aboard.

They immediately cut down our sails so we couldn't escape. A furious battle followed. Twice, we drove them back from our bloodstained decks. In the end, though, their greater numbers won the day.

Three of our crew were killed and eight wounded. The rest of us, myself included, laid down our arms and surrendered. I had heard dreadful stories of what happened to those captured by the pirates of Morocco, and my heart was full of dread as I entered the port of Salé in chains.

CHAPTER 2

Slavery and Shipwreck

I was now a slave. Because I was young and strong, the pirate captain kept me for himself. The rest of the crew were sent to the court of the Emperor, far inland. There they were beaten, starved, and given the most dreadful work to do.

I was more fortunate. My master was a fair man and treated me well—as long as I did as I was told. I tried hard to please him, though this was not always easy at first because I did not speak his language.

With no one to talk to, I grew miserable. Once again, I realized how foolish I had been to ignore my father's advice. *How good it would be to be safe*

in a lawyer's office in York, I thought, *instead of lying here, a slave in a foreign land!*

Somehow, I had to escape. My best chance would be to sail on the pirate ship and hope it was captured by an English, French, Spanish, or Portuguese vessel. But whenever my master went to sea, he left me at home to watch over his house.

Then, after two years as a prisoner, an opportunity finally came.

My master liked
fishing. Once a
week, he went out in
a small boat to see
what he could catch.
He always took me
and a boy named
Xury with him.

One day, my master decided to
serve his dinner guests with fresh fish.
Since he was too busy to go himself,
he ordered Xury and myself and a
strong guard to do the fishing for him.
I persuaded the guard to put food and
weapons on board, in case we got lost in
fog or were attacked by bandits.

When we were out at sea, I threw
the guard overboard and ordered him
to swim for the shore. I told Xury that

I'd put him overboard, too, unless he accepted me as his master. He gave a broad grin—and the deal was done.

Xury and I sailed together for three weeks. From time to time, we went ashore for food and fresh water. Once, we were attacked by a huge lion, which I shot dead.

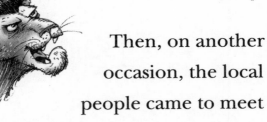

Then, on another occasion, the local people came to meet us with food and presents.

After many adventures, we found ourselves near the Cape Verde islands. Here, we were rescued by a Portuguese ship. I was free at last!

During all my adventures, I have been helped by some very kind people. One of these was the friendly captain of the Portuguese ship that rescued us. He was going to Brazil, and I offered him all I had to take us with him.

The good captain refused my money. In fact, he paid *me*! He gave me eighty gold coins for the boat I had stolen

from the pirate captain. He offered sixty more coins if I would sell him Xury.

Of course, I refused. But when the boy said he didn't mind because it would help me, I sadly let him go. I also sold the skin of the lion I had shot.

In Brazil, I bought as much land as I could afford. It became known as Crusoe's Farm, or "Plantation." For the next three years, I lived as a "planter." I grew corn, tobacco, and sugarcane, and I became quite well off.

Looking back, these years proved very useful. First, I learned how to grow crops. Second, because my plantation was far from any town, I became used to living on my own.

As you will see, these turned out to be very valuable lessons.

You've probably guessed that something terrible was about to happen to me. You're right—and this is how it began …

After four years in Brazil, my plantation had become very successful. Before I sailed from England, all those years ago, you may remember that I left two hundred pounds with the widow of my first captain. I now got a Portuguese friend to bring half of that money to Brazil.

I used it to buy servants and workers, and my plantation flourished even more.

Crusoe's tobacco fetched the highest prices in the market. *Ah-ha, father!* I said to myself. *If I had*  *followed your advice, I'd be stuck in an office in York. Instead, look at me now! I'm a wealthy landowner.*

I was proud of what I had achieved. And pride, they rightly say, comes before a fall.

Not content with my fortune, I wanted more. Many of the plantations in Brazil used slave workers. These poor men and women were bought in Africa and shipped to South America. Because I had been to Guinea, in Africa, my friends suggested I go there, buy slaves, and bring them back to Brazil.

I would, they said, make a lot of money.

On the first of September, 1659, I
boarded a ship sailing for Guinea. It was
precisely eight years since I'd left my poor
parents. I still felt guilty, and someone—
maybe God—was about to punish me.

The voyage was all storms. The first
lasted for twelve long days. Our ship was
tossed around like a cork. One sailor
was killed, and our young cabin boy was
washed overboard and drowned.

The vessel was so badly damaged that
we decided to get it repaired in Barbados.
After that, we would sail on to Guinea.
Tragically, we did not even reach Barbados.

The second storm was much fiercer
than the first. It ripped the sails from the
masts and snapped the masts themselves.
Vast waves thundered over the ship's sides,
filling it with water. We were unable to

steer, and the roaring tempest drove us on
to a foaming bar of sand.

Certain that the ship would break up,
we launched the lifeboat. What a mistake!
A gigantic wave, as big as a mountain,
caught our little craft and swallowed it up.

I struggled to the surface. After a long
battle, more dead than alive, I reached
the shore and collapsed.

CHAPTER 3

Marooned!

When I came to, I thanked God for saving me. The rest of the crew had all drowned. I was stranded in a strange place with only the clothes I was wearing. Terrified, I climbed into a tree and fell asleep.

The morning broke calm and clear. I saw that our ship had not broken up but was stuck on a sandbank a little way from the shore. If the crew had stayed on board, they would have been saved!

I pulled myself together, swam out to the vessel, and climbed aboard. I collected food and other things I needed, and ferried them back to dry land on a raft. Over the next few days, I made eleven more trips to the ship.

As well as tools, guns, and ammunition, I saved the captain's dog and two cats. They were the only company I had. I laughed when I found gold and silver coins—what use was money to me now?

After my twelfth trip, another great storm blew up during the night. I went down to the shore the next morning and looked out to sea. The wreck had disappeared. I had no choice but to make the best of my new situation.

When I first came ashore, I climbed a
tall hill and looked around. Two things
became clear. First, I was on an island.
Second, as I could see no sign of other
human beings, it was a desert island.
I was marooned!

Right, I thought, *I'd better make myself safe.*
I moved the tent I'd made to a site higher
up, and dug a cave into the hillside behind
it. It made an excellent storage area.

I circled my little settlement with a high
fence. The only way in was by a ladder,

which I pulled up after me. I camouflaged the fence, too, so from the outside it looked like a small wood.

I went hunting every morning. To my delight, I found there were goats on the island. I shot some for food and tried, unsuccessfully, to tame a kid. Nevertheless, I still hoped to set up a small farm on the island one day.

To keep track of time, I kept a diary. When I saw how the days, weeks, and months passed, I felt very miserable. *Come on, Crusoe*, I said to myself. *You're the fortunate one— think of what happened to the rest of the crew!*

I had never been very religious. But now, thinking about how I had been saved, I began to pray more. It made me feel good. I set up a wooden cross and carved a notch on it for each of my days on the island.

It's remarkable what you can do if you have to. I carved tools from hard wood and learned how to make storage barrels.

My best invention was a lamp. I put goat fat in a dish, stuck in a piece of string as a wick—and lit it. It worked! My nights were now not so dark and scary.

As time went by, my diet became more varied. I discovered which birds and animals were good to eat. I also

killed and ate a turtle, and I cooked its eggs. They were delicious.

The biscuits I brought from the ship did not last long. I couldn't make more because rats had been in my corn. I had to throw it out. Imagine my amazement, therefore, when I found that the grains had planted themselves and were starting to grow!

I now had the farm I had dreamed of, with small fields of wheat and rice.

My island had wet and dry seasons.
Starting in June, heavy rain fell daily.
It sometimes kept me indoors from dawn
to dusk.

It was during one of these days that I
suddenly felt cold. *That's strange*, I thought.
*I'm in the tropics where the temperature is
always high. Even the rain is warm.*

I then realized the truth: I was seriously
ill. Fever hit me like the wave that had
swamped our boat. I shivered, agonizing
pains gripping my arms and legs. Sweat
poured from me like the rain off the
roof of my tent.

I had neither doctor nor medicine.
For days, I lay groaning on my rough bed,
unable to move.

Fortunately, I gradually recovered, and
for a while, I felt fine. But the fever came

sweeping back, worse than before. This
time, I had terrible nightmares, always
with my parents in them. *Oh, what an
ungrateful fool I am!* I cried to myself.

I was surely going to die.

But, through God's mercy, I survived.
When able to move, I mixed rum and
tobacco into a kind of medicine. I have
no idea why, but it made me stronger and
helped me return to my usual life.

When I was well, I decided to get to know my island better. I call it "my" island because I saw myself as a sort of king. My dog and the cats were my subjects.

The number of my subjects grew when the cats had kittens. Looking after my animals, hunting, and tending to the crops in my fields, I was kept a busy man.

Exploring parts of the island I hadn't visited before, I came across many new fruits. There were oranges, lemons, grapes, and juicy melons. By drying the grapes, I produced delicious raisins. I also found some wild sugarcane. I chopped it down, took out the juicy sap— and enjoyed sweet drinks with my meals.

The best thing I brought home from my travels was a bird. I managed to

capture a young parrot. It was a most
beautiful creature with feathers of blue,
green, and gleaming gold.

When I got back to my house (as
I called it), I fashioned a birdcage out of
sticks and put my parrot inside. Slowly,
one step at a time, I taught it how to
speak. What a joy it was to hear words not
spoken by myself!

CHAPTER 4

My Island Kingdom

Two years had now passed since my shipwreck. On one of my trips around my kingdom, I had climbed a hill and spied land in the distance. It was between fifty and sixty miles away.

I wondered about what I had seen. Who lived there? If they were Spaniards, I was safe. But I had heard sailors tell of other people living in this part of the world. Cannibals! I shuddered at the idea of meeting those who ate human flesh.

Nevertheless, I thought, *there's only one way of finding out who lives over there. I'll pay them a visit.*

To cross the sea, I needed a large boat. I chose a suitable tree and chopped it down. It took five months to cut off the branches, smooth down the trunk, and hollow out the inside. In the end, I had a fine boat.

What an idiot! I hadn't worked out how to get it into the water. It was far too big to move on my own. I tried digging a canal to the sea, but it was impossible.

Furious with myself for being so stupid, I gave up. I had to leave my lovely boat rotting in the forest.

By my fifth year on the island, my clothes were in tatters. They hardly covered me. I got wet in the rain and burned by the sun. I needed new ones.

The shirts and trousers I had rescued from the wreck fitted quite well. But my only hat had fallen to pieces. I looked at the materials around me. Goat skin.

Whenever I killed a goat, I took off the skin and left it to dry. Now, having cut out a suitable shape, I sewed it into a neat cap. In fact, it was better than my old hat because it was completely waterproof.

If a goat skin hat can keep the rain out, I reasoned, *why not a complete suit?* I set to work with scissors, needle, and thread. The result might not have been the height of fashion, but it was just what I needed. Who was there to care what I looked like?

My wardrobe lacked just one item: an umbrella. It took me ages to make one like those I had seen in South America. But using goat skin and pieces of wood, I eventually made a perfect sunshade that also kept off the rain.

Five more years passed. My life continued as before, caring for my animals, growing crops, and repairing my furniture and tools. But the image of the distant land remained at the back of my mind.

I needed a new boat.

This time, I made it small enough to get into the water. I fitted it with a mast and sail, and attached my umbrella at the stern. All was ready for a voyage of exploration.

On the first two days, I didn't go far, as I needed to learn how to handle my little craft. By the third day, I was ready to sail out to sea. This was a big mistake.

A powerful current gripped the boat and carried it far from the shore. I wrestled with the sails and prayed for a good wind. Only after struggling for hours did I manage to return safely to the island.

I was utterly exhausted. I tied up my boat, lay down, and fell asleep. I was woken by a voice crying in my ear: "Robin, Robin Crusoe! Poor Robin Crusoe! Where have you been?"

Petrified, I sprang to my feet and looked round. It was just Pol, my parrot, welcoming me home!

Months passed. I was so frightened
by my boat trip that I did not go sailing
again for a long time. Instead, I stayed at
home and worked on my house and farm.

I learned to weave baskets. On one
of my trips, I had found tobacco plants.
I cut the leaves, dried them in the sun,

and in the evenings, smoked them in a handmade pipe. At such moments, I dreamed I was back in England.

Because my gunpowder was running low, I stopped shooting and took up trapping. Gradually, I built up a big herd of goats. It provided me with all the milk, butter, and cheese I needed.

After a year, I plucked up the courage to take my boat out again. I was extremely careful to avoid currents and dangerous rocks. I had had enough of shipwrecks!

Sailing around my tiny kingdom, a thought came to me. As king, I ought to know precisely what I owned. So, when I got home, I made a list of all my possessions.

It was a silly thing to do—but it comforted me when I was about to receive a terrible shock.

When you live on your own for fifteen years, as I had, your mind plays tricks on you. You imagine things that are not there. That's why what happened to me one fine day almost drove me crazy.

I was walking along the beach, not thinking about anything very important. Suddenly, I stopped. There was something on the ground before me.

One pace away, clear as daylight, was a human footprint in the sand—not a track made by someone walking, just one single print. I stood frozen to the spot and stared in terror.

The foot was bigger than mine, so it couldn't have been made by me. Then, by whom? A one-legged monster? The devil, haunting me for behaving so badly toward my parents all those years ago?

I had no answer. I rushed back to my camp and pulled up the ladder. That night, I didn't sleep a wink. After fifteen years of solitude, I was no longer alone.

My only thought was to defend myself. I built a second fence around my home and looked behind me nervously whenever I went out. All I could do was wait.

CHAPTER 5

Cannibals!

The footprint in the sand changed my life on the island forever. But if the print was bad, what I next saw was much worse.

Every day, I climbed the hill near my home to look for boats. Two years after I had seen the footprint, I spied a canoe disappearing into the distance. I hurried to the shore to see if the visitors had left anything behind.

As well as footprints, dreadful remains lay upon the sand. Skulls, bones, and bits of human bodies were scattered near a dark patch where a fire had burned.

My island—my kingdom—was the place where cannibals cooked and ate their poor prisoners!

The sight horrified me. For years afterward, I hardly left my home. I had added new fortifications, making it more like a fortress than a house.

The cannibals never left my mind. I didn't fire a gun in case they heard its noise. I didn't light a fire in case they saw its smoke. I didn't even chop wood in case the sound echoed down to the beach where they held their foul feasts.

My despair deepened when, after a long and faithful friendship, my old dog finally died. These were hard times.

If the cannibals returned, I promised myself that I would attack them. I'd shoot them all dead.

Then I thought again ...

God had created the world and everything in it. Since he had made the cannibals, who was I to condemn them? I hated what they did, but they did not know any better. God himself would judge them, not me.

I did not set eyes on the cannibals until the December of my twenty-third year on the island. Seeing the smoke of their fire, I crept down to the shore and hid to watch their ghastly banquet. I shivered in horror.

*

After that, the savages, as I called them, did not return for a year. In the meantime, a tragedy occurred. A great Spanish ship

was wrecked upon the rocks of my island.
Not one of the crew survived.

I swam out to the wreck, looking
for things that might be of use. There
wasn't much, though I did recover bags
of money and some gold bars. More
welcome was the half-drowned ship's dog
that struggled ashore and lay at my feet.

I now had a new companion—even the
worst disasters can bring a little comfort.

I dreaded that the cannibals might learn about me and hunt me down. I had to get away. But how? My only hope was to capture a savage who could lead me to safety on the mainland.

As it turned out, I had no need to capture anyone.

Two years after I had watched the grizzly banquet, the cannibals returned. Thirty of them came in five canoes. I armed myself and went down to the shore.

The savages had brought two prisoners to feast upon. As I watched, they killed one and chopped him up for cooking. The other, finding himself unguarded, made a dash for freedom. Half a dozen cannibals set off in pursuit.

To my dismay, I found that the victim was heading toward me! He was a strong runner, and three of his pursuers soon gave up. Another dropped out when the runaway swam across a creek. He was now almost upon me.

I had to save him. Raising my gun, I took aim and fired. The two pursuers dropped to the sand. The man they had been chasing stared in amazement. Then, very slowly, stopping to kneel every few steps, he advanced toward me.

I lowered my gun and smiled.

When the runaway reached me, he knelt and kissed my foot. Later, he explained that this was to say, "Thank you. You have saved my life, and I will be your servant."

I looked up to see that one of the pursuers had only been stunned. He was advancing toward us. Before I could shoot, my new friend grabbed my sword and cut off the attacker's head.

Using sign language, we agreed to cover up the dead bodies to hide them from the other cannibals. That done, I gestured to my friend to follow and then we set out for my fortress home.

Just by chance, I had found the ideal companion. He was tall, good-looking, and intelligent. We got along extremely well. Though he was my servant, I saw him more as a friend.

I called him "Friday," because that was the day of the week on which we had met. He was not used to wearing clothes but liked it when I dressed him in some taken from the wreck. It didn't take him long to pick up a few words of English, either.

One of the first things I told him was that I thought that eating people was wrong. He understood straight away.

At first, Friday slept in a tent outside my main home. However, I quickly realized he loved me, and he was the best and truest friend I ever had. I was happy to share my house with such a man.

I found, to my dismay, that Friday had himself eaten human flesh. Now that he agreed this was wrong, I gave him different meat. I was relieved to find he liked goat and hare.

Friday was terrified of my gun. He had seen what it could do and believed it was magic, like a god! I even found him talking to it, asking it not to kill him. I explained that it was not alive but was only a tool. After I showed him how it worked, he became a good hunter.

Once Friday could speak fluently—which he managed very swiftly—he told me many things. He described the currents of the sea, life with his own people, and how he had been captured. If we had a boat, he said, we could easily get to the mainland.

We talked about religion, too. I explained Christianity to him, and he described his own beliefs to me. I found them very strange, indeed, and I hoped that one day he would become a Christian like me.

CHAPTER 6

Home at Last

Friday and I lived in peace for three years. When he said there were Europeans on the mainland, I was eager to go there. We built a boat big enough to carry us both. But before we set out, six cannibal canoes appeared for another grizzly feast.

Friday wanted to attack them with our guns. I hesitated. But when I saw that one of the prisoners was a European, I changed my mind, and we both opened fire. They screamed and ran about wildly.

I rushed in and rescued the European man, who turned out to be Spanish. In the chaos, four cannibals jumped into a canoe and fled. Friday leaped into another canoe to chase them.

"Master!" he cried. "Come look!"

There, tied up on the bottom of the canoe, was another prisoner. His father!

Friday and I led the rescued men to my fortress home. After a hearty meal, they soon recovered. Friday asked his father whether the cannibals would return with an army to destroy us.

The old man shook his head. No, he said. They were too frightened by our guns ever to return.

For the moment, we were safe.

This was our plan.
Friday's father and
the Spaniard would
use our new boat
to collect the other
Spaniards from
the mainland.

Together, we would then build an even
bigger boat and sail to safety.

However, before the boat came back
from the mainland, my adventures took
another strange twist. An English ship
anchored close to my island!

But something was not right. In the
small boat that came ashore were eight
sailors and three prisoners. Friday and
I sneaked down to the shore to take
a closer look. At midday, the sailors
went into the woods for a nap. We crept

up to the prisoners and set them free.

You should have seen the looks on their faces! Who was this wild-looking man, and who was his friend, they asked?

I explained about my twenty-seven years on the island, and they told me their story. The ship's crew had mutinied. They had captured the ship's captain and two honest companions, and planned to maroon them on my island. These were the three men we had set free.

"Right," I said. "If we help you, you must do exactly as I say and then take us back to England."

The captain immediately agreed.

Step one was capturing the men asleep in the woods. This was easily done, though one of them was shot dead when he tried to warn the others. The captain said he'd spare those who swore loyalty to him. They all did.

Next, we had to deal with the twenty-six mutineers on the ship. When their mates did not return, ten of them came ashore. After leading them on a wild

goose chase, we ambushed them. Two, we shot dead, the rest surrendered.

Finally, with a bit of trickery and bravery, we recaptured the ship. I ordered the leader of the mutiny, Will Atkins, to be hanged. The captain and I reckoned that twelve of the rest of the crew were reliable.

The others, we chose to leave on my island. I explained how to look after the animals and the farm. I also told them that some Spaniards would soon be joining them from the mainland.

One or two of them complained. I reminded them that if they returned with us, they might well be hanged for mutiny. "And anyway," I added, "This island was my home for twenty-seven years. You'll find it's not such a bad place, after all!"

We set sail on the nineteenth of December, 1686. As we were hauling up the anchor, two of the men we had left on the island swam to the ship and begged to be taken aboard. I agreed, though they were whipped for taking part in the mutiny.

By the time we reached England, I had been away for thirty-five years. So much had changed. For a start, we had a new government and a new king.

To my great sadness and regret, I learned that both my parents had died. My father had left me nothing in his will because he assumed I was dead. But I remembered my plantation in Brazil and went to Portugal with Friday to find out what had happened to it.

On arriving in Lisbon, the capital of Portugal, I learned that my plantation had made a small fortune. I was a rich man!

At once, I rewarded everyone who had looked after my business while I was away. That done, I planned how to take my money back to England.

Should I go by sea? No way! I had had more than my fair share of shipwrecks, and I didn't want to risk another.

A group of five of us gathered for the long journey through Spain and France to England. Friday looked about in amazement—the fields, the buildings, the people were all so new and strange to him.

Knowing my luck, you will not be surprised to hear that I had one last adventure. It happened when we reached the lofty Pyrenees mountains. It was winter, and the roads were deep in snow. Poor Friday had never felt so cold in his life. His teeth chattered like castanets, day and night.

The icy weather drove all sorts of wild animals out of the hills, toward the villages. On one lonely road, we were faced by a lumbering bear. Luckily for me, Friday, who had hunted these animals

at home with bows and arrows, shot the
beast dead.

Later still, we were surrounded by a
pack of snarling wolves. I ordered the
men to light a ring of fire around us and
shoot from behind it. The idea worked,
and we were saved.

And so, we reached England at last. There, I settled down, married, and had a lovely family. Friday stayed with me, and when I looked at him, I dreamed of further adventures.

But that is all for the moment. The rest, as they say, is another story.